Snarf

Borgle

Amoeboid

Rocket

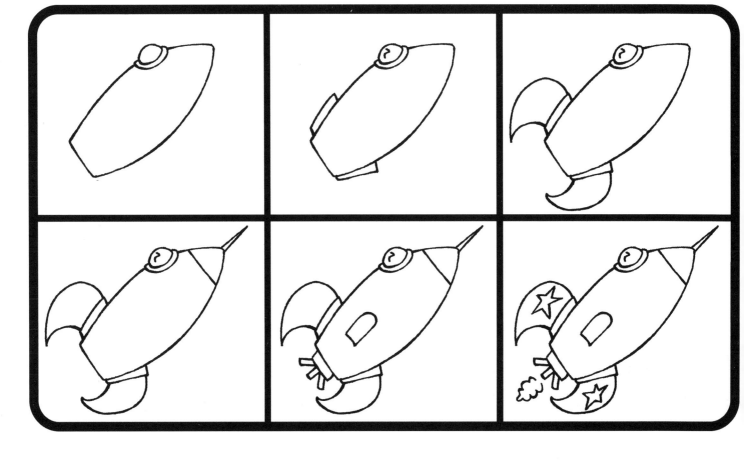

Predator

Flying Saucer

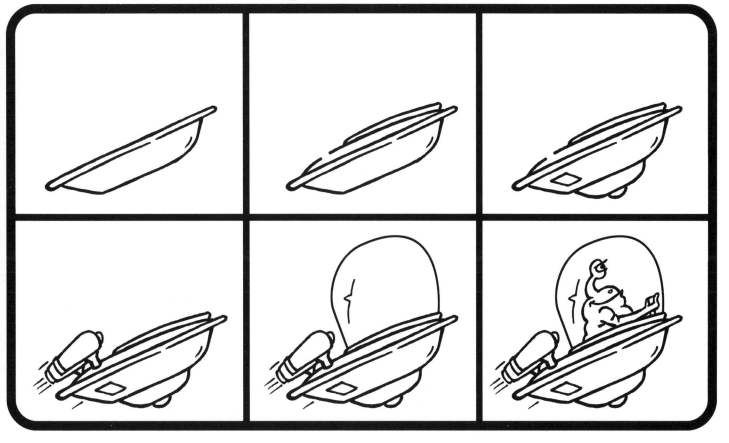

Zoom

Battle Droid

Asteroidus

Jabber

Lightspeed

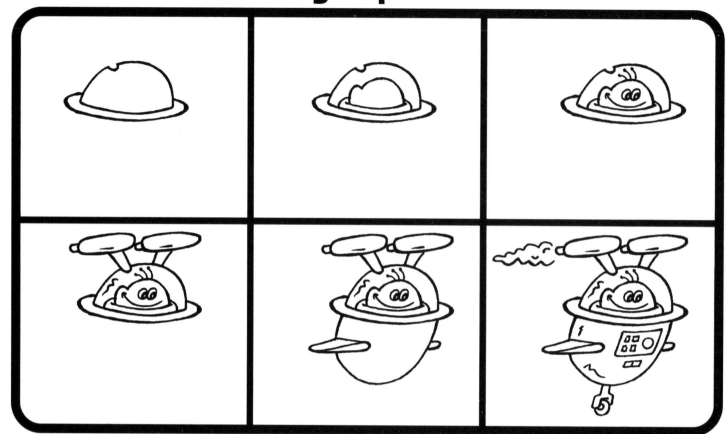

Neutreno

Laser

Worker Droid

Space Monkey

Alien X

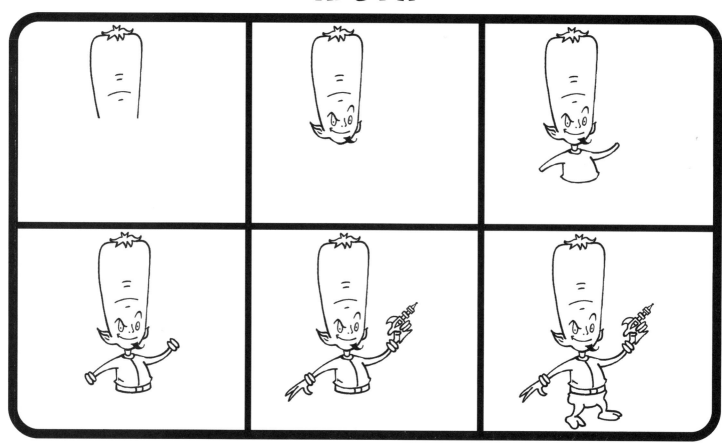

Electro

Nebulus

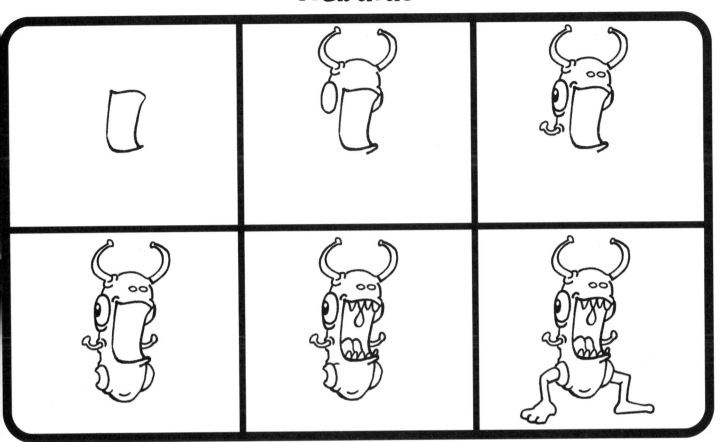

Starship Destroyer

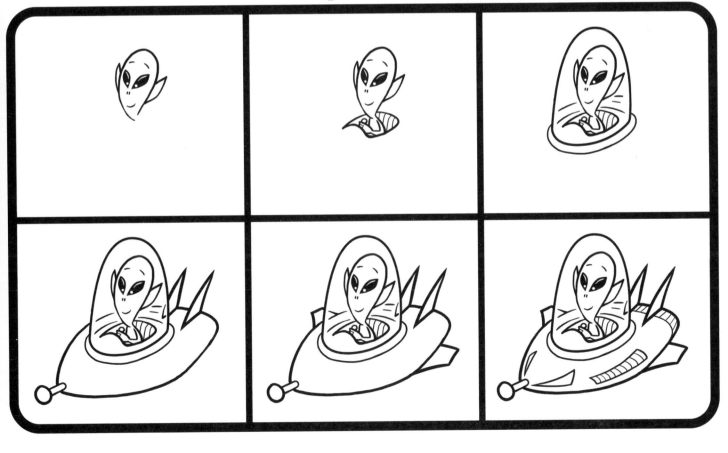

Space Pirate

Gravitoid

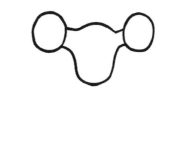

Warp

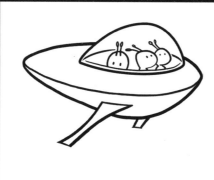

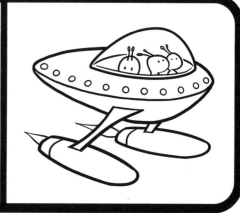

Space Dog

Bugle

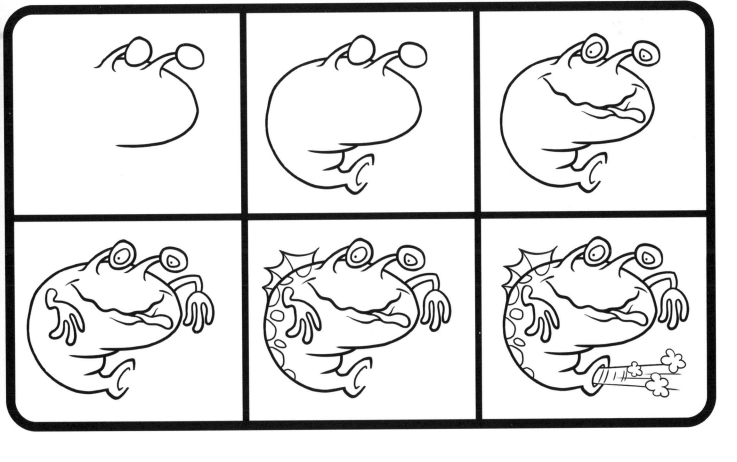

Apocalypse

Mollusk

Arachnid

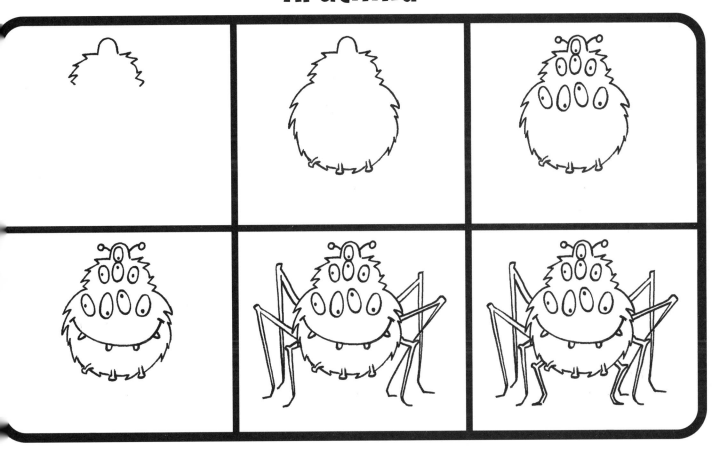

Beagle

Blaster

Bounty Hunter

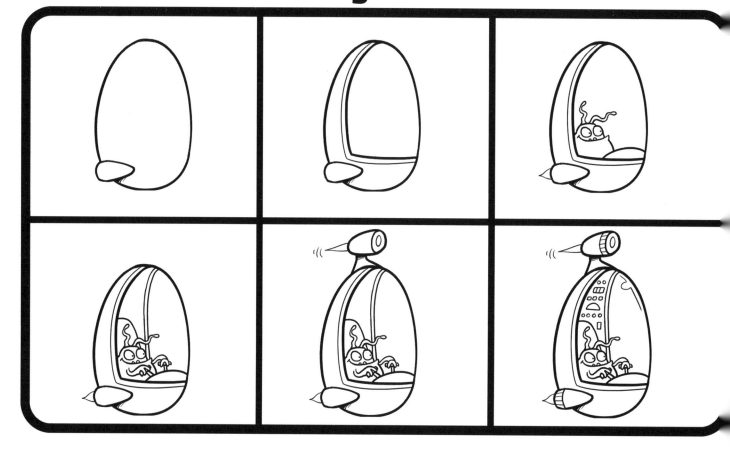

Zap

Starcrawler

Matrix

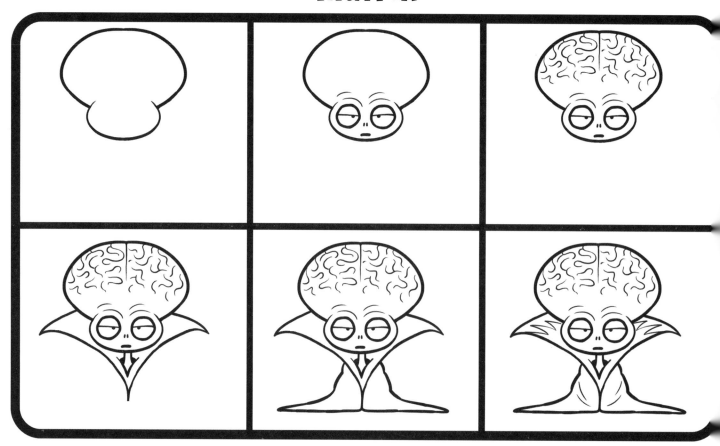

Infantry Droid

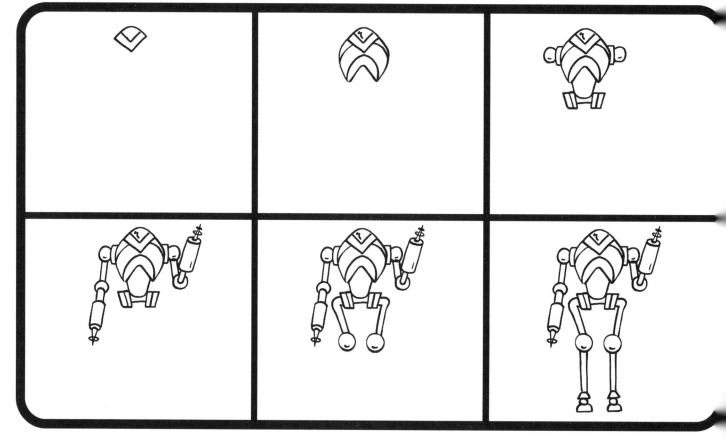

Nemotoad

Ice Planet Trooper

Star Man

Plasma

Space Troll

Space Sumo

Red Planet Beast

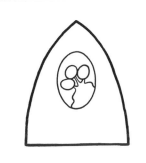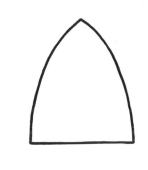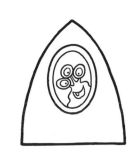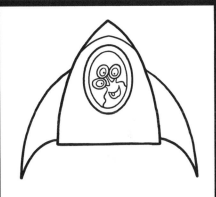

Fraggle

Crater Face

Saturn Hydra

Solar Windsurfer

Alien Pet

Vampoid

Space Rock Monster

Alien Medic

Space Raider

Alien Invader

Space Ghost

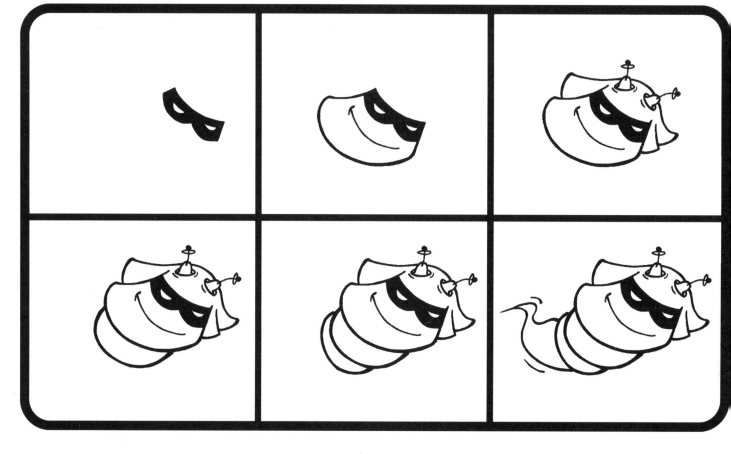